Ready-to-Go Reproducibles
STANDARDIZED TEST SKILL BUILDERS
TERRANOVA
Grade 5

New York • Toronto • London • Auckland • Sydney
Mexico City • New Delhi • Hong Kong

Cover design by Kelli Thompson
Interior design by Creative Pages
Interior illustrations by Kate Flanagan

ISBN 0-439-21119-0

Printed in the U.S.A.

Contents

Introduction to Teachers

We all know how important it is for students to do well on tests. This book is one in a series designed to help you help your students become better test takers. In the past few years, many statewide tests and national standardized tests have undergone significant changes, not just in *what* they measure but also in *how* they measure content and skills. The examples and practice tests in this book reflect the latest developments in testing, particularly in the CTBS® *TerraNova*. Features include:

- Reading/Language Arts and Math tests organized by themes
- A variety of different types of literature and informational texts
- A combination of multiple-choice and short-answer questions
- Open-ended Math problems with multiple solutions

This book covers the Reading/Language Arts and Math skills tested on the CTBS® *TerraNova* for Grade 5, and it uses the same kinds of test-item formats.

Practice Tests

There are two Practice Tests in this book, one for Reading/Language Arts and one for Math. Each test is divided into two parts for easy administration. Features of each Practice Test include:

- Sample items for students to work through
- Hints and test-taking tips on how to answer each type of question
- Explanations of the correct answers
- Reminders to help students during an actual test

Procedures

We recommend that you work through the sample items on each Practice Test with your students. Discuss the questions and how to get the right answers, and then have students take each part of the test. Plan on 25–30 minutes to administer each part of a Practice Test. Have students mark their answers on the test directly, or—for the multiple-choice sections—have students use a copy of the answer sheet on page 45. (For the Math test, students will need a ruler for measuring in inches and in centimeters. The use of calculators is optional but is not recommended.)

Use the Answer Keys at the back of the book to score each test, or have students score the tests themselves. Mark the answer to each item as correct or incorrect. Have students record their scores on a copy of the Scoring Chart (page 48) to help them keep track of their own progress. After each testing session, make sure students have ample opportunity to study their own tests and learn from any mistakes they might have made.

Students who complete the practice tests in this book will become familiar with the kinds of questions they will see on the CTBS® *TerraNova* and other tests, and they will have a new arsenal of techniques and strategies for getting better test scores.

Reading/Language Arts

}HINT: Before you read, take a quick look at the questions so you know what to look for in the story.

SAMPLES

Directions Read each passage. Choose the best answer to each question.

Donkey's Ears

Long, long ago, King Midas of Phrygia was chosen to judge a musical contest between Apollo and Pan. The powerful Apollo played the most beautiful tune anyone had ever heard. Then Pan, a minor god of the forest, played a lovely song. King Midas foolishly decided that Pan was the winner of the contest. Apollo was so upset by this decision that he changed King Midas's ears to donkey ears.

Most of the time, King Midas was able to keep his ears hidden under a large hat. The only person who saw the ears was the barber who cut the king's hair, and he was sworn to secrecy.

After a while, though, the barber could not hold the secret inside any longer. He went out to a large, grassy field and dug a hole. Then he yelled his secret into the hole: "King Midas has donkey's ears!" Feeling much better, the barber filled in the hole again and returned home. But, the next spring, reeds grew out of that very spot in the field. When the wind blew, the reeds whispered the barber's words for everyone to hear.

}HINT: Look for clues in the story to help figure out the answers.

A **What probably happened next?**
- Ⓐ King Midas got his normal ears back.
- Ⓑ The barber turned into a donkey.
- Ⓒ People learned of King Midas's ears.
- Ⓓ Pan and Apollo had another contest.

B **You can tell from this story that**
- Ⓕ King Midas was a good judge
- Ⓖ the barber was a brave man
- Ⓗ Apollo was more powerful than Pan
- Ⓙ King Midas was very clever

C **Why did the barber yell into the hole?**
- Ⓐ He could not keep the secret inside.
- Ⓑ He wanted everyone to know the secret.
- Ⓒ He was trying to find someone.
- Ⓓ He thought Pan would help him.

D **Find the word that best completes the sentence.**

The shepherd found a flute and _____ a tune.
- Ⓕ play
- Ⓖ playing
- Ⓗ played
- Ⓙ have played

Standardized Test Skill Builders—TerraNova, Grade 5

Scholastic Professional Books

Predicting Winter

Do you wonder how cold it will be next winter, or how much snow will fall? If you live in or near Tennessee, you can find out.

Helen Lane, who lives in Crab Orchard, Tennessee, has been predicting winters for more than 50 years. Every fall, Ms. Lane checks the signs of nature to <u>forecast</u> what the coming winter will be like. First she looks at the woolly worms, which are brown and black caterpillars. If the woolly worms are more black than brown, the winter will be cold and snowy. Then she checks the hornets and spiders. If the hornets build nests close to the ground and the spiders make webs close together, the winter will be harsh. Cold weather is coming if animals have thicker-than-normal fur.

People in Tennessee have counted on Helen Lane's wisdom for a long time. Now, as Ms. Lane approaches 80 years old, they will come to depend on her daughter Melinda instead. Melinda will check the signs of winter each year and let people know what to expect.

HINT: Look back at the passage to find the answer to each question.

E   What is this passage mostly about?
- Ⓐ the town of Crab Orchard, Tennessee
- Ⓑ what woolly worms look like
- Ⓒ Helen Lane's predictions of winter
- Ⓓ how hornets build their nests

F   Which of these signs suggests that winter will be cold and snowy?
- Ⓕ Spiders make their webs far apart.
- Ⓖ The hornets stop building nests.
- Ⓗ Wild animals have thin fur.
- Ⓙ The woolly worms are mostly black.

G   From this passage, you can tell that the word <u>forecast</u> means to
- Ⓐ stay close together
- Ⓑ change in direction
- Ⓒ depend on
- Ⓓ predict beforehand

H   Find the sentence that is complete and is written correctly.
- Ⓕ Winter began early this year.
- Ⓖ Looking for signs of snow.
- Ⓗ Helen Lane, for more than 50 years.
- Ⓙ At the beginning of October.

I   Find three mistakes in the paragraph below. Draw a line through each mistake. Above the line, write the word or words correctly.

> In the first week of December. A blizzard hitting
>
> the state. A total of 22 inches of snow falls in one day.

J   What happens in the story "Donkey's Ears"? Write one sentence that summarizes the plot of the story.

_____

_____

Finding the Answers

Questions A–D are about the story, "Donkey's Ears." To answer question A, you must predict what probably happened next. The end of the story says, "The reeds whispered the barber's words for everyone to hear." Based on this clue, the most likely answer is **C**, "People learned of King Midas's ears."

To answer question B, you must look for clues. The story says that Apollo was powerful, that Pan was a "minor god," and that King Midas "foolishly" chose Pan as the winner. These clues suggest that Apollo was more powerful than Pan. Answer **H** is correct.

For question C, you must draw a conclusion about why the barber yelled into the hole. The story says that he was sworn to secrecy, but he could not keep the secret inside any longer. Answer **A** is correct.

Question D is about using verbs correctly. The verb you choose should be in the same tense as *found*. "The shepherd *found* a flute and played a tune." The best answer is **H**, "played."

Reading/Language Arts

HINT: Before you read, take a quick look at the questions so you know what to look for in the story.

SAMPLES

Directions Read each passage. Choose the best answer to each question.

Donkey's Ears

Long, long ago, King Midas of Phrygia was chosen to judge a musical contest between Apollo and Pan. The powerful Apollo played the most beautiful tune anyone had ever heard. Then Pan, a minor god of the forest, played a lovely song. King Midas foolishly decided that Pan was the winner of the contest. Apollo was so upset by this decision that he changed King Midas's ears to donkey ears.

Most of the time, King Midas was able to keep his ears hidden under a large hat. The only person who saw the ears was the barber who cut the king's hair, and he was sworn to secrecy.

After a while, though, the barber could not hold the secret inside any longer. He went out to a large, grassy field and dug a hole. Then he yelled his secret into the hole: "King Midas has donkey's ears!" Feeling much better, the barber filled in the hole again and returned home. But, the next spring, reeds grew out of that very spot in the field. When the wind blew, the reeds whispered the barber's words for everyone to hear.

HINT: Look for clues in the story to help figure out the answers.

A What probably happened next?
Ⓐ King Midas got his normal ears back.
Ⓑ The barber turned into a donkey.
Ⓒ People learned of King Midas's ears.
Ⓓ Pan and Apollo had another contest.

B You can tell from this story that
Ⓕ King Midas was a good judge
Ⓖ the barber was a brave man
Ⓗ Apollo was more powerful than Pan
Ⓙ King Midas was very clever

C Why did the barber yell into the hole?
Ⓐ He could not keep the secret inside.
Ⓑ He wanted everyone to know the secret.
Ⓒ He was trying to find someone.
Ⓓ He thought Pan would help him.

D Find the word that best completes the sentence.

The shepherd found a flute and _____ a tune.
Ⓕ play
Ⓖ playing
Ⓗ played
Ⓙ have played

Scholastic Professional Books

Questions E–H refer to the nonfiction article, "Predicting Winter." To answer question E, you must decide what the passage is mostly about. You are looking for the main topic. This passage focuses on Ms. Helen Lane and how she predicts what the coming winter will be like. The correct answer is **C**.

To answer Question F, you must find the supporting detail that tells which sign suggests a cold and snowy winter to come. The passage states that if woolly worms are more black than brown, then the winter will be cold and snowy, so the correct answer is **J**.

For Question G, you must figure out what *forecast* means from the way it is used in the passage. The first paragraph says that Ms. Lane checks the signs of nature and predicts what the winter will be like, so *forecast* must mean "predict beforehand," answer **D**.

Question H is about writing complete sentences. A complete sentence has a subject, which tells what the sentence is about, and a predicate, which tells what the subject is or does. Answer **F** is correct because it is the only choice that has both a subject (*winter*) and a predicate (*began*).

Predicting Winter

Do you wonder how cold it will be next winter, or how much snow will fall? If you live in or near Tennessee, you can find out.

Helen Lane, who lives in Crab Orchard, Tennessee, has been predicting winters for more than 50 years. Every fall, Ms. Lane checks the signs of nature to <u>forecast</u> what the coming winter will be like. First she looks at the woolly worms, which are brown and black caterpillars. If the woolly worms are more black than brown, the winter will be cold and snowy. Then she checks the hornets and spiders. If the hornets build nests close to the ground and the spiders make webs close together, the winter will be harsh. Cold weather is coming if animals have thicker-than-normal fur.

People in Tennessee have counted on Helen Lane's wisdom for a long time. Now, as Ms. Lane approaches 80 years old, they will come to depend on her daughter Melinda instead. Melinda will check the signs of winter each year and let people know what to expect.

HINT: Look back at the passage to find the answer to each question.

E What is this passage mostly about?
- Ⓐ the town of Crab Orchard, Tennessee
- Ⓑ what woolly worms look like
- Ⓒ Helen Lane's predictions of winter
- Ⓓ how hornets build their nests

F Which of these signs suggests that winter will be cold and snowy?
- Ⓕ Spiders make their webs far apart.
- Ⓖ The hornets stop building nests.
- Ⓗ Wild animals have thin fur.
- Ⓙ The woolly worms are mostly black.

G From this passage, you can tell that the word <u>forecast</u> means to
- Ⓐ stay close together
- Ⓑ change in direction
- Ⓒ depend on
- Ⓓ predict beforehand

H Find the sentence that is complete and is written correctly.
- Ⓕ Winter began early this year.
- Ⓖ Looking for signs of snow.
- Ⓗ Helen Lane, for more than 50 years.
- Ⓙ At the beginning of October.

I Find three mistakes in the paragraph below. Draw a line through each mistake. Above the line, write the word or words correctly.

> In the first week of December. A blizzard hitting the state. A total of 22 inches of snow falls in one day.

J What happens in the story "Donkey's Ears"? Write one sentence that summarizes the plot of the story.

_____

In Question I, you must correct three errors in the way the paragraph is written. The answer below shows one way to correct the errors.

> December, a
> In the first week of ~~December. A~~ blizzard ~~hitting~~ hit
> the state. A total of 22 inches of snow ~~falls~~ fell in one day.

To answer Question J, you must write a sentence that summarizes what happens in "Donkey's Ears." For example, "When King Midas chooses Pan as the winner of a musical contest, Apollo changes the king's ears to donkey ears."

Scholastic Professional Books

Test-Taking Tips and Reminders for Reading/Language Arts

As you take the Practice Test, try these strategies to help you score better.

✓ Before you read a passage, take a quick look at the questions so you know what to look for.

✓ Read the title and the whole passage carefully.

✓ Look at the picture. Sometimes a picture gives clues to what the passage is about.

✓ To find the main idea, decide what the whole passage is mostly about.

✓ Look for clues in the passage to help answer the questions.

✓ Go back to the passage to find the information you need to answer each question. Key words (such as *who, what, when, where, why, alike,* and *different*) can help you figure out what to look for.

✓ When you draw a conclusion, look for two or more details in the passage to support your answer.

✓ Look for clues in the passage to figure out the meaning of a word you don't know. Then read the answer choices carefully before you choose an answer.

✓ To determine the author's purpose, ask why the author wrote a passage. Stories are usually written to entertain or to teach a lesson. Factual articles are usually written to give information or to persuade the reader.

✓ To identify the sequence of events in a passage, look for signal words, such as *first, then, later, finally, next,* and *last.*

✓ For fill-in-the-blank questions, try each answer choice in the blank to see which one makes the most sense.

✓ When you have to write an answer, read the question carefully. Think about how to answer the question before you begin writing. Look for key words in the question to help you decide what your answer should be.

Reading/Language Arts: Practice Test

Part 1: New Ideas

Directions
This part of the test is about trying new ideas. Read each passage. Then choose the best answer to each question.

> HINT: Before you read the passage, take a quick look at the questions so you know what to look for.

Grandpa's Garden

"It looks like the deer have been raiding our garden again," said Grandpa, pointing to the fresh tracks around the lettuce patch. "It's frustrating to put so much work into a garden, only to have the deer feast on it. That fence is pretty useless," he added, eyeing the thin wire fence around the garden.

"Let's build a scarecrow," said Josh. "Maybe if we can trick the deer into believing there's someone in the garden, they'll stay out."

Grandpa agreed that a scarecrow was a fine idea and sent Josh to the barn for some hay. They stuffed the hay into one of Grandpa's old flannel shirts and an old pair of his overalls. Then they put an old straw hat on the scarecrow's soccer ball head. Stepping back to look at their work, they both burst out laughing.

"He looks like you," said Josh, his eyes darting back and forth between Grandpa and the scarecrow.

Grandpa chuckled. "He's a bit more handsome, I think. Let's just hope he gets the job done."

Just before breakfast the next morning when Josh looked out the window, he spotted two young does in the garden. "Grandpa, come quick!" he cried,

racing out of the house toward the garden. "Go on, shoo!" he yelled, running and waving his arms. In one graceful movement, the two deer leaped over the thin wire fence. They turned back once to look at Josh before dashing for cover in the nearby forest.

Josh frowned at the scarecrow. "A lot of good you were," he said.

"I guess we'll have to come up with a better plan," said Grandpa as he checked the garden. "It doesn't look as though they got much this time. Come on, let's go plan our next move over breakfast."

Grandpa and Josh were tossing ideas around at the breakfast table when Grandma suggested they try placing bars of soap around the garden. "I've heard that really works," she said. Josh and

Grandpa both looked doubtful. "Well, it can't be any worse than that scarecrow that doesn't scare anything," she huffed.

"Sure, Mum, we'll do that," said Grandpa, winking at Josh. "Which soap do you recommend?" He kicked Josh gently under the table.

Josh bowed his head and tried not to laugh.

Later that afternoon, after they had failed to come up with a better idea, Josh and Grandpa drove into town to buy a few dozen bars of scented soap. They spent the rest of the afternoon "planting" soap all around the garden. Grandpa cut long, sturdy branches and sharpened both ends. Josh stuck a bar of soap on one end and "planted" the other end into the ground. When they were through, Grandpa shook his head and said, "If this works, I swear I'll eat my hat."

"I'll remember you said that," said Grandma. Josh and Grandpa both started in surprise. They had not heard Grandma approach. "On the other hand," she said, "I think I'd rather you boys took me out for a nice dinner in town—you know, by way of saying thank you for a great idea." Chuckling to herself, she turned and headed back to the house.

A few days later, Josh and Grandpa stood on the porch waiting for Grandma. Grandpa looked toward the garden and scratched his head. "Still no deer, huh?"

"Nope," answered Josh, "not one."

"Well, I hate to admit it," said Grandpa, "but your grandmother was right."

As if on cue, Grandma appeared on the porch dressed in her Sunday best. She handed Grandpa his hat. "I believe you were going to eat this," she said.

Grandpa chuckled. "I think I like the second choice better," he said, offering her his arm. "We have reservations for six o'clock."

1 **What will most likely happen next?**
 Ⓐ Grandpa will eat his hat.
 Ⓑ Grandpa and Josh will take Grandma to see the garden.
 Ⓒ Grandma will go into the house to make dinner.
 Ⓓ Grandpa and Josh will take Grandma out to dinner.

> HINT: Look for clues in the passage to help answer the questions.

2 **You can tell that Grandma and Grandpa live**
 Ⓕ near the ocean   Ⓗ in a city
 Ⓖ in the country   Ⓙ in a desert

3 **Why is Grandpa trying to keep the deer out of the garden?**
 Ⓐ He doesn't want the deer to eat everything in the garden.
 Ⓑ He's afraid the deer will get sick if they eat the weeds in the garden.
 Ⓒ He doesn't want the deer to break down the fence.
 Ⓓ He's afraid Grandma will make him eat his hat for dinner if he doesn't.

4   In what month does this story probably take place?

     Ⓕ January   Ⓗ July

     Ⓖ February   Ⓙ November

HINT: When you draw a conclusion, look for two or more details in the passage to support it.

5   Which statement about deer is most likely accurate?

     Ⓐ Deer are easily fooled by scarecrows.

     Ⓑ Deer never feed alone.

     Ⓒ Deer cannot find enough food to eat in the forest.

     Ⓓ Deer stay away from strongly scented soap.

6   Why did Grandpa wink at Josh and kick him under the table?

     Ⓕ He was angry at Josh because of his bad table manners.

     Ⓖ He wanted to let Josh know that he was teasing Grandma.

     Ⓗ He got something in his eye and wanted Josh to take a look at it.

     Ⓙ He wanted Josh to pay attention to what he was saying.

Directions

For 7 and 8, choose the word or words that best complete each sentence.

HINT: Try each answer choice in the sentence to see which one makes the most sense.

7   The deer raided the garden and _____ all the lettuce.

     Ⓐ eat   Ⓒ ate

     Ⓑ will eat   Ⓓ eaten

8   Josh and Grandpa _____ determined to keep the deer out of the garden.

     Ⓕ being   Ⓗ were

     Ⓖ is   Ⓙ was

For 9 and 10, choose the correct spelling of the word to complete each sentence.

9   Dad _____ me how to build a scarecrow.

     Ⓐ teached   Ⓒ taugt

     Ⓑ taut   Ⓓ taught

10   Always use _____ when you are close to wild animals.

     Ⓕ caution   Ⓗ causion

     Ⓖ caushion   Ⓙ coution

Scholastic Professional Books

The Shoemaker's Luck

Many years ago, a young shoemaker named Jacob moved to the city to make his fortune. "The city is filled with people," he thought, "and they all need shoes." So Jacob rented a shop on a busy street

HINT: Read the title and the whole passage carefully.

and set to work making shoes, which he proudly displayed in the shop window.

Unfortunately for Jacob, there were a dozen other shoemakers in the city, and all of them made better shoes than Jacob. Weeks passed, and Jacob did not have even one customer. Unsold shoes piled up in the window.

Jacob's bad luck spurred him to work harder. From sunup to sundown, he made pair after pair of shoes. "Practice will make me a better shoemaker," he decided, "and then people will buy my shoes."

Now it happened that, unknown to Jacob, a pair of mice lived in the shop walls. They felt sorry for Jacob and wished they could help him somehow. "Jacob should move to a village where he is the only shoemaker," suggested one mouse. "Then people would buy his shoes."

"You're right," answered the other mouse, "but how can we persuade him to leave the city?"

The two mice put their heads together and came up with a plan. As soon as Jacob left the shop that evening, the mice jumped into the pile of unsold shoes and gnawed holes in each and every one. When Jacob returned the next morning, he sobbed at the sight of the chewed-up shoes. "I've had awful luck in this shop. It's time for me to move on," he said. "Perhaps I'll have more success as a village shoemaker."

With that, Jacob started packing up his tools. But as he did, a woman stopped to look in the shop window. Then she hurried inside, picked up a shredded shoe, and exclaimed, "I must have a pair of these smart-looking sandals!"

Amazed and pleased, Jacob sold the shoes to the woman. Then he went back to packing. But a moment later, a man entered the shop. He, too, asked to buy sandals. After that, more and more customers came into the shop for sandals. In an hour, Jacob had sold every pair of shredded shoes.

Jacob wasted no time wondering what he should do next. He unpacked his tools and set to work making sandals. From that day on, Jacob always had many eager customers. After all, he was the only sandal maker in the city.

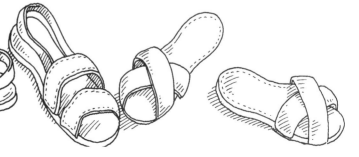

Scholastic Professional Books

11 Where does this story take place?
   Ⓐ in a small village
   Ⓑ on a farm
   Ⓒ in a city
   Ⓓ on a country road

HINT: Go back to the passage to find the information you need to answer each question.

12 Based on what you read in this story, which word pair best fits in this sentence?

As a shoemaker, Jacob was _____ but _____.
   Ⓕ skillful . . . greedy
   Ⓖ determined . . . unsuccessful
   Ⓗ lazy . . . lucky
   Ⓙ rich . . . unhappy

13 When the two mice "put their heads together," they
   Ⓐ worked together to solve a problem
   Ⓑ looked into each other's eyes
   Ⓒ posed for a picture together
   Ⓓ whispered secrets to each other

HINT: Read all the answer choices before you choose one.

14 What happened after Jacob left the shop one evening?
   Ⓕ Someone stole all his shoes.
   Ⓖ Two mice made some new boots for him.
   Ⓗ A woman bought all his shoes.
   Ⓙ Two mice chewed holes in all his shoes.

15 Which was the most important reason Jacob had for deciding to leave the city?
   Ⓐ The mice did not like him.
   Ⓑ He could not make a living.
   Ⓒ He had to make sandals.
   Ⓓ He did not like to work hard.

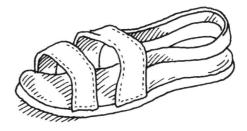

Scholastic Professional Books

16 When people started buying his shoes, Jacob felt
  Ⓕ pleased
  Ⓖ annoyed
  Ⓗ hurt
  Ⓙ sneaky

17 What lesson does this story teach?
  Ⓐ Keep your troubles to yourself.
  Ⓑ Happiness is better than wealth.
  Ⓒ Don't accept help from others.
  Ⓓ Be willing to try new things.

Directions
For 18 and 19, choose the word that best completes each sentence.

> HINT: Try each answer choice in the sentence to see which one makes sense.

18 I like these sandals because _____ are comfortable.
  Ⓕ them   Ⓗ its
  Ⓖ it   Ⓙ they

19 One woman bought shoes for _____ daughters.
  Ⓐ her   Ⓒ she
  Ⓑ hers   Ⓓ they

20 Choose the complete sentence that is written correctly.
  Ⓕ Growing up in a small village.
  Ⓖ The shoemaker opened a shop in the city.
  Ⓗ Jacob and his three brothers.
  Ⓙ Everyone who wanted to buy a pair of sandals.

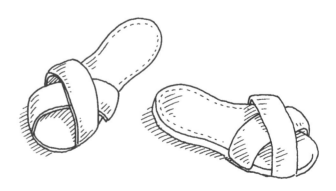

Let's Write

Write your answer to each of these questions about "Grandpa's Garden" and "The Shoemaker's Luck."

HINT: Read each question carefully. Think about how to answer the question before you begin writing.

21 In "Grandpa's Garden," what problem did Josh and Grandpa have?

_____ _____

_____

22 How did Josh and Grandpa feel about Grandma's idea at first, and how did they feel about it a few days later?

At first, they _____

_____

_____

A few days later, they _____

_____

_____

23 In "The Shoemaker's Luck," what was Jacob's problem, and how did he solve it?

_____

_____

_____

_____

Scholastic Professional Books

24   How does each of these stories fit the theme of "New Ideas"? Explain.

_____

_____

_____

_____

25   Here is a letter written by a student. Find six mistakes in grammar, capitalization, and punctuation. Draw a line through each mistake. Above the line, write the word or words correctly.

> **HINT:** Check your work when you have finished.

Dear mom and dad.

    The train ride was fun but it was very long. When I arrived in Boston on saturday, Uncle Harry met me at the station. "Its wonderful to see you, he said." I was glad to see him, too.

                love always

                Miranda

Reading/Language Arts: Practice Test

Part 2: Personal Goals

Directions
This part of the test is about young people who work toward their personal goals. Read each passage. Then choose the best answer to each question.

ΗΙΝΤ: Read the title and the whole passage carefully.

A Rising Star

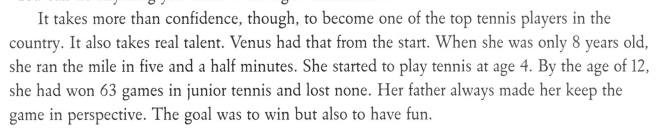

Venus Williams was born in Compton, California, on June 17, 1980. She is the fourth daughter of Richard and Oracene Williams. From the beginning, her father predicted that she would be a tennis champion.

Life in Compton wasn't easy. Gang wars and crime were common. Gunshots sometimes sounded in the background as Venus and her younger sister, Serena, played tennis every day on a run-down public court, watched over by their father. But Venus was confident. Her mother always said, "You can do anything you want. Nothing is unattainable."

It takes more than confidence, though, to become one of the top tennis players in the country. It also takes real talent. Venus had that from the start. When she was only 8 years old, she ran the mile in five and a half minutes. She started to play tennis at age 4. By the age of 12, she had won 63 games in junior tennis and lost none. Her father always made her keep the game in perspective. The goal was to win but also to have fun.

People noticed Venus's talent, but they doubted she would be a success. How could she? Her main coach was her father, who had no background in tennis. She also wasn't allowed to play as much as other young players were. Her father limited her playing time so that she could do well in school.

Venus wasn't bothered by doubt. The tall girl with braces and braids just grinned and echoed her father's prediction. She and her little sister would be the two best players in the world one day.

Venus Williams turned professional at age 14. She reached the finals of the U.S. Open at age 17. By the age of 18 she was ranked twelfth in the world, and just a year later she was ranked third. Before turning 20, she had made millions of dollars in prize money and millions more in product endorsements.

So far, none of this has fazed the 6'2" athlete with the 127-mile-per-hour serve. Speaking for herself and Serena, she says, "We're showing that we're capable of doing what we always said we would." She's also still having a lot of fun.

Scholastic Professional Books

26 **What is the main topic of this passage?**

    Ⓕ growing up in Compton, California

    Ⓖ Venus Williams' career in tennis

    Ⓗ how to have fun playing tennis

    Ⓙ Richard Williams' job as a coach

HINT: To find the main idea, decide what the whole passage is mostly about.

27 **If you wanted to find more information about Venus Williams, you would be most likely to find it in**

    Ⓐ a textbook

    Ⓑ an encyclopedia

    Ⓒ newspapers and magazines

    Ⓓ a dictionary

28 **From this passage, what can you conclude about Venus Williams?**

    Ⓕ She has little faith in her younger sister's abilities.

    Ⓖ She cares about nothing except winning at tennis.

    Ⓗ She secretly wished to be something other than a tennis player.

    Ⓙ She was inspired to succeed by both of her parents.

29 **Which of these events occurred last?**

    Ⓐ Venus turned professional.

    Ⓑ Venus reached the finals of the U.S. Open.

    Ⓒ Venus ran a mile in under six minutes.

    Ⓓ Venus won her sixty-third game in junior tennis.

HINT: To identify the sequence of events, look for signal words or numbers.

30 **Which is the best summary of this passage?**

    Ⓕ Venus Williams has become a champion tennis player, as her father predicted she would.

    Ⓖ Venus Williams and her sister Serena learned to play tennis.

    Ⓗ Richard and Oracene Williams had five daughters, two of whom play tennis.

    Ⓙ Many female tennis champions today are fairly young.

31 The author's main purpose in this selection is to

   Ⓐ entertain the reader with a funny story

   Ⓑ teach a lesson about playing tennis

   Ⓒ persuade the reader to start playing tennis

   Ⓓ give information about Venus Williams

HINT: To determine the author's purpose, ask why the author wrote the passage.

32 Which sentence is written correctly?

   Ⓕ Serena Williams also a powerful tennis player.

   Ⓖ Serena Williams playing tennis powerfully, too.

   Ⓗ Serena Williams is a tennis player she is powerful too.

   Ⓙ Serena Williams is also a powerful tennis player.

33 Which sentence is correctly capitalized and punctuated?

   Ⓐ Venus Williams, a tennis player, also loves to surf.

   Ⓑ Venus please serve the ball to your opponent.

   Ⓒ Venus is being interviewed, the reporter is from Australia.

   Ⓓ Venuses older sisters are Yetunde, Isha, and Lyndrea.

34 Jimmy wrote these two sentences in a paragraph about tennis. Which is the best way to combine these two sentences into one?

HINT: Read all the answer choices before you choose one.

Mom and I went to a tennis tournament.
Mom and I saw Venus Williams play.

   Ⓕ Mom and I, at a tennis tournament, went to see Venus Williams play.

   Ⓖ Mom and I saw Venus Williams when she went to a tennis tournament.

   Ⓗ Mom and I went to a tennis tournament and saw Venus Williams play.

   Ⓙ When Mom and I went to a tennis tournament, Mom and I saw Venus Williams play.

35 Jimmy was reading an article about tennis. Under which heading of the article would he probably find information about how tennis was first invented?

   Ⓐ Rules of the Game

   Ⓑ Early History

   Ⓒ Professional Players

   Ⓓ U.S. Tennis Association

Scholastic Professional Books

No Skateboarding

On Wednesday, a new sign appeared in front of Williamson's Hardware. It read: "No Skateboarding & No Skating." In a letter that was published in the local paper, Mr. Williamson explained that kids skating around his parking lot made it hard for his customers to drive in and park safely. His customers were afraid of hitting one of the skaters, and they also were afraid of being hit by a skater while walking from their cars to the store. People were complaining, he explained, and so he had to ban skating from his lot altogether.

Liza was furious. "That isn't fair!" she complained to her parents over dinner that night. "The Williamson's lot is the best place in town to skate, and we don't bother anybody. We always watch out for cars, and we never run into people who are walking. Mr. Williamson just doesn't like kids. He just wants the kids to go away because he's mean."

"Mean, is he?" her mother asked softly. "That's an interesting statement. Have you ever talked to him?"

"Talked to Mr. Williamson?" Liza answered. "Never! Why would I want to talk to someone who hates me?"

Liza's mother thought for a moment before responding. "I'll tell you what," she said. "You go to the store tomorrow and talk with Mr. Williamson. I don't mean yell at him or be rude to him or act like you think he hates you. Talk to him as an adult. Make an appointment to see him, so he is expecting you, and then talk with him in a reasonable way. If, when you come home, you still think he's banning skating just to be mean, then I'll go talk to him myself."

"Fine," Liza said, "but it won't do any good."

The next night at dinner, Liza seemed pleased about something. At last her mother asked, "Well, did you talk to Mr. Williamson today?"

Liza nodded. "Right after school. I told him about how his lot was the best for skating, and how we all try hard not to get in the way of his customers. I thought he would yell at me or something, but he didn't. He said he understood my frustration, but then he said that a lot of his customers, especially the older ones, were nervous with kids skating around the lot. Even if we stay out of the way, they're afraid to come to his store. They're afraid they might hit someone."

"So how did it end?" her mother asked.

"I couldn't believe it," Liza said. "We struck a deal. He's going to bulldoze the lot behind his store and donate a whole load of cement. If I can get enough kids together to do the work, he'll let us turn that lot into an outdoor skating area."

Liza grinned. "I've got to call my friends tonight after dinner," she said. "We have a lot of work to do." Then she looked at her mother. "Mr. Williamson is really cool," she added with just the hint of a smirk. "I don't know *why* you said he was mean."

36 Liza's main purpose for meeting with Mr. Williamson was to

    Ⓕ persuade him to let kids skate in his parking lot

    Ⓖ ask him why he hated children

    Ⓗ compare his parking lot to other lots in the city

    Ⓙ tell him that she understood his point of view

HINT: When you draw a conclusion, look for two or more details in the passage to support it.

37 What can you tell about Mr. Williamson from this passage?

    Ⓐ He is very mean.

    Ⓑ He wants to help the kids.

    Ⓒ He does not listen to others.

    Ⓓ He cares only about his customers.

38 Which detail supports the idea that Liza realized she was wrong about Mr. Williamson?

    Ⓕ She told him that his lot was the best place for skating.

    Ⓖ She said that he just wanted the kids to go away.

    Ⓗ She told him that all the kids tried not to get in the way of his customers.

    Ⓙ She admitted that he was really cool.

39 The most important reason for Liza to talk with Mr. Williamson was to

    Ⓐ clear up some misunderstandings

    Ⓑ show her support for his hardware store

    Ⓒ satisfy her mother's request

    Ⓓ prove that he disliked children

40 Mr. Williamson will _____ kids to wear helmets when they skate. Which word suggests that Mr. Williamson will try to make a helpful suggestion?

    Ⓕ order   Ⓗ lecture

    Ⓖ advise   Ⓙ beg

Directions

Look at the underlined part of each sentence. Choose the answer that shows the correct capitalization and punctuation for the underlined part. If the underlined part is written correctly, mark "Correct as it is."

41 The doctor <u>said "you</u> could have been badly hurt."

    Ⓐ said, "you   Ⓒ said, "You

    Ⓑ said "You   Ⓓ Correct as it is

42 Mr. Grant, <u>Liza's neighbor</u>, will help build the skating area.

    Ⓕ Liza's Neighbor   Ⓗ Lizas's neighbor

    Ⓖ Lizas' neighbor   Ⓙ Correct as it is

One of Liza's classmates wrote a story about a boy who had a magic bicycle. Read the story. It has some mistakes that need correcting.

Freddy and the Magic Bike

(1) Freddy was riding down the hill he heard a siren. (2) A fire truck came around the corner. (3) Freddy wondered where the fire truck was going. (4) He pressed the secret button on the handlebars. (5) The bike immediately lifted off the ground. (6) Freddy flew into the air, turned the bike around, and raced after the fire truck.

---

43 **Which is the best way to write Sentence 2?**
Ⓐ A fire truck comes around the corner.
Ⓑ When a fire truck came around the corner.
Ⓒ A fire truck coming around the corner.
Ⓓ Best as it is

HINT: Try each answer choice to see which one makes the most sense.

44 **Where would this sentence best fit in the story?**

It was traveling very fast.

Ⓕ after Sentence 1
Ⓖ after Sentence 2
Ⓗ after Sentence 4
Ⓙ after Sentence 5

45 **Which sentence has two complete thoughts and should be rewritten?**
Ⓐ Sentence 1
Ⓑ Sentence 3
Ⓒ Sentence 5
Ⓓ Sentence 6

Scholastic Professional Books

Let's Write

Write your answer to each of these questions about "A Rising Star" and "No Skateboarding."

46 In "A Rising Star," what did Venus Williams' father think was important for her to remember?

HINT: Read each question carefully. Look for key words to help you decide what your answer should be.

_____

_____

_____

47 Write two or three sentences describing Venus Williams. What kind of person is she?

_____

_____

_____

48 In "No Skateboarding," what was Mr. Williamson's response to Liza's request? Write a brief summary of his response.

HINT: Check your work for correct grammar, capitalization, and punctuation.

_____

_____

_____

Read the poster below. Then write your answer to each question.

Soccer Tryouts

Do you want to play soccer? Are you in fifth or sixth grade? We will be holding tryouts for all boys and girls interested in playing soccer this year.

When: Saturday, September 10, at 10:00 A.M.

Where: Norwich Elementary School

Be there on time! Bring a signed permission form with you. Parents who are interested in helping to coach the team should also attend the first tryout.

---

49   Write the information that is most important for you to know if you plan to try out for soccer.

HINT: Go back to the poster to find the information you need.

_____

_____

50   Write the information that is important for parents.

_____

_____

Scholastic Professional Books

Mathematics

SAMPLES

Directions
Choose the best answer to each question. If your answer is not given, mark "None of these."

HINT: Read each problem carefully.

A Sam is hiking the Summit Trail in a state park. The trail is 8.2 kilometers long. He has hiked 4.5 kilometers so far. How much farther does he have to hike?

Ⓐ 3.7 km
Ⓑ 3.8 km
Ⓒ 4.7 km
Ⓓ 12.7 km
Ⓔ None of these

HINT: Look for key words and numbers to help solve each problem.

B Kara gets on the school bus at 7:25. The ride to school takes 40 minutes. Which clock shows the time she should arrive at school?

Ⓕ

Ⓖ

Ⓗ

Ⓙ

C Arjun bought 19 video games for $58.95 each. Which numbers give the best estimate of the total cost?

Ⓐ 10 × $50
Ⓑ 20 × $50
Ⓒ 10 × $60
Ⓓ 20 × $60

HINT: To estimate, round each number to the nearest 10.

Scholastic Professional Books

D Mr. Mason wants to put a fence around the perimeter of his rectangular vegetable garden. What is the perimeter of the garden?

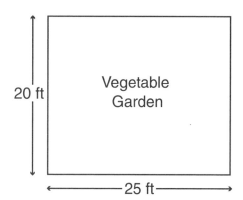

HINT: Check your work to make sure you have computed correctly.

Ⓕ 45 ft
Ⓖ 100 ft
Ⓗ 250 ft
Ⓙ 500 ft
Ⓚ None of these

E Fifth graders voted on their favorite subjects and recorded their votes on a tally chart. On the grid below, make a bar graph to show these results. Include labels and a title.

Votes per Subject

Science	ꞮꞮꞮꞮꞮ ꞮꞮꞮꞮꞮ ꞮꞮ
English	ꞮꞮꞮꞮꞮ ꞮꞮꞮꞮ
Gym	ꞮꞮꞮꞮꞮ ꞮꞮꞮꞮꞮ ꞮꞮꞮꞮꞮ

Finding the Answers

To answer Question A, you must decide whether to add, subtract, multiply, or divide. As you read the problem, look for key words and numbers to help you decide. The trail is 8.2 kilometers long, and Sam has hiked 4.5 kilometers. To find *how much farther* he has to go, you must subtract: 8.2 km − 4.5 km = 3.7 km. Answer **A** is correct.

In Question B, you must determine what time Kara should arrive at school and then find the clock that shows that time. She gets on the bus at 7:25, and the ride to school takes 40 minutes. You can find the time of her arrival by counting 40 minutes on the clock, or by adding 7 hours 25 minutes + 40 minutes. The total is 7 hours 65 minutes. Since 1 hour = 60 minutes, the total is 8 hours 5 minutes. She should have arrived at 8:05, so answer **J** is correct.

For Question C, you need to choose the numbers that will give the best estimate for 19 × $58.95. To find an estimate, round each number to the nearest 10. In this problem, the best estimate would be 20 × $60. Answer **D** is correct.

Question D involves finding the perimeter of the garden. The formula for finding the perimeter of a rectangle is P = 2 × (length + width). The diagram shows that the length is 25 ft and the width is 20 ft. The perimeter is 2 × (25 ft + 20 ft), or 2 × 45 ft = 90 ft. Since "90 ft" is not one of the answers given, you would mark answer **K**, "None of these."

In question E, you need to draw a bar graph showing the results of the vote. Your graph should look similar to the graph below, which shows that 12 students voted for Science, 9 for English, and 15 for Gym.

Mathematics

SAMPLES

Directions
Choose the best answer to each question. If your answer is not given, mark "None of these."

> HINT: Read each problem carefully.

A Sam is hiking the Summit Trail in a state park. The trail is 8.2 kilometers long. He has hiked 4.5 kilometers so far. How much farther does he have to hike?
- Ⓐ 3.7 km
- Ⓑ 3.8 km
- Ⓒ 4.7 km
- Ⓓ 12.7 km
- Ⓔ None of these

> HINT: Look for key words and numbers to help solve each problem.

B Kara gets on the school bus at 7:25. The ride to school takes 40 minutes. Which clock shows the time she should arrive at school?

Ⓕ Ⓖ Ⓗ Ⓙ

C Arjun bought 19 video games for $58.95 each. Which numbers give the best estimate of the total cost?
- Ⓐ 10 × $50
- Ⓑ 20 × $50
- Ⓒ 10 × $60
- Ⓓ 20 × $60

> HINT: To estimate, round each number to the nearest 10.

Standardized Test Skill Builders—TerraNova, Grade 5   27

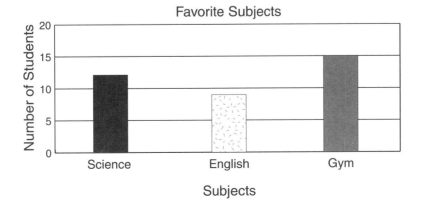

Favorite Subjects

Number of Students (vertical axis: 0, 5, 10, 15, 20)

Subjects (Science, English, Gym)

Test-Taking Tips and Reminders for Mathematics

As you take the Practice Test, try these strategies to help you score better.

✓ Read each problem carefully to make sure you know what it is asking for.

✓ Look for key words to help you decide whether you should add, subtract, multiply, or divide.

✓ Write a number sentence to help you solve each problem.

✓ Always rewrite fractions in their simplest form.

✓ When computing with decimals, be sure to place the decimal points correctly.

✓ Try each answer choice to find the one that is correct.

✓ Eliminate any answers that you know are wrong. Then, if you are still not sure of the answer, make your best guess.

✓ To estimate, round each number to the nearest 10, 100, or 1000.

✓ Check your work to make sure you have computed correctly.

✓ Look back at the table, chart, or graph to find the information you need for each question.

✓ Draw your own picture if it will help you solve the problem.

✓ Check your answer to be sure it makes sense.

Mathematics: Practice Test

Part 1

Directions

Choose the best answer to each question. If your answer is not given, mark "None of these."

Mr. Henner's class visited the state fair on Student Day this year. Do Numbers 1–7 about the fair.

1 On Monday, a total of 1362 people went to the fair. What is that number rounded to the nearest 100?

Ⓐ 1300
Ⓑ 1360
Ⓒ 1370
Ⓓ 1400

> **HINT:** Check your work to make sure you have computed correctly.

2 The school bus traveled 0.6 miles from the garage to the school and 3.5 miles from the school to the fair. How far did the bus travel in all?

Ⓕ 1.9 miles
Ⓖ 3.1 miles
Ⓗ 4.1 miles
Ⓙ 4.2 miles
Ⓚ None of these

3 The exhibit hall at the fair is divided into three sections. Two-fifths of the exhibits are in Section B of the hall, and another two-fifths are in section C. What fraction of the exhibits are located in Section A?

Ⓐ $\frac{4}{5}$
Ⓑ $\frac{4}{10}$
Ⓒ $\frac{1}{5}$
Ⓓ $\frac{4}{25}$
Ⓔ None of these

4 When Cal and Maria bought lunch, their total bill was $11.19. They gave the cashier $20.25. How much change should they receive?

   Ⓕ $9.06

   Ⓖ $9.14

   Ⓗ $10.06

   Ⓙ $10.44

   Ⓚ None of these

HINT: Write a number sentence to help you solve each problem.

5 This year there were 648 rabbits entered in competitions at the fair. The rabbits were kept in separate cages in an exhibition hall. There were 8 equal rows of rabbit cages in all. How many cages were in each row?

   Ⓐ 61

   Ⓑ 81

   Ⓒ 108

   Ⓓ 640

   Ⓔ None of these

6 This year's prize-winning pumpkin weighed 357 pounds. That is exactly 3 times the weight of the third-place pumpkin. How much did the third-place pumpkin weigh?

   Ⓕ 112 pounds

   Ⓖ 119 pounds

   Ⓗ 354 pounds

   Ⓙ 1071 pounds

   Ⓚ None of these

HINT: Try each answer choice to find the one that is correct.

7 The pig races attracted 2345 people during the morning and 1937 people in the afternoon. How many people watched the pig races in all?

   Ⓐ 3272

   Ⓑ 3612

   Ⓒ 4272

   Ⓓ 4382

   Ⓔ None of these

8 A chicken farm produces about 1400 eggs per day. Of that number, about 950 are judged good enough to be sold. How many eggs are <u>not</u> good enough to be sold?

   Ⓕ 550

   Ⓖ 505

   Ⓗ 500

   Ⓙ 450

   Ⓚ None of these

HINT: Look for key words to help you decide whether to add, subtract, multiply, or divide.

9 Wendy's mom buys peanuts by the pound to feed the squirrels. If peanuts cost 59 cents per pound, <u>about</u> how much does Wendy's mom pay for 20 pounds of peanuts?

   Ⓐ $5

   Ⓑ $7

   Ⓒ $10

   Ⓓ $12

HINT: To estimate, round each number to the nearest 10.

10 Chad and his mom used 2 pounds of apples to make 3 quarts of homemade applesauce. About how many pounds of apples would they need to make 10 quarts of applesauce?

   Ⓕ between 4 and 5

   Ⓖ less than 4

   Ⓗ between 6 and 7

   Ⓙ more than 7

11 Sunny Day orange juice costs between 9 and 10 cents an ounce. Which is the best estimate of the cost of a 16-ounce carton of Sunny Day?

   Ⓐ $1.00

   Ⓑ $1.50

   Ⓒ $1.80

   Ⓓ $2.00

12 At the post office, Charles bought 12 stamps for $0.32 each and a postcard for $0.20. Which number sentence could be used to find how much Charles spent in all?

   Ⓕ $(12 \times \$0.32) + \$0.20 = \square$

   Ⓖ $12 \times (\$0.32 + \$0.20) = \square$

   Ⓗ $(12 \div \$0.32) + \$0.20 = \square$

   Ⓙ $12 + \$0.32 + \$0.20 = \square$

13   Read the rule. If you put the number 24 in the *In* column, what should you put in the *Out* column?

RULE: Divide by 3, then add 4.

  (A) 10
  (B) 12
  (C) 14
  (D) 16

IN	OUT
9	7
12	8
15	9

Rico has just moved to town. Polly drew a grid map of their neighborhood to teach him how to get around. Answer questions 14 and 15 about the map.

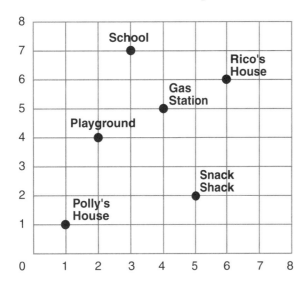

14   What is located at (4, 5)?
  (F) Rico's house
  (G) Polly's house
  (H) the gas station
  (J) the playground

15   If Rico moved one point to the right and three points up from the playground, where would he be?
  (A) his house
  (B) the Snack Shack
  (C) the school
  (D) Polly's house

> HINT: Look back at the map to find the information you need.

Lena and Kayla are making dream catchers for a craft fair. Do Numbers 16–20.

16 Supplies for the dream catchers cost $14.88. If Lena and Kayla split the cost equally, how much would each girl pay?
- Ⓕ $7.44
- Ⓖ $7.88
- Ⓗ $14.48
- Ⓙ $14.88
- Ⓚ None of these

17 Lena had 4 rolls of brown string. There were 10.5 feet of string in each roll. How many feet of brown string did Lena have?
- Ⓐ 40 feet
- Ⓑ 40.2 feet
- Ⓒ 41.5 feet
- Ⓓ 45 feet
- Ⓔ None of these

18 Later Kayla decided to make some more dream catchers to give away as gifts. She spent exactly $6.00 more on supplies. Which items did she buy?

- Ⓕ two packages of beads
- Ⓖ a ball of yarn and a package of leather lacing
- Ⓗ two packages of feathers
- Ⓙ a package of beads and a package of feathers

19 Lena is making a bead chain with the pattern shown.

If the pattern continues, which kind of bead should come next?

- Ⓐ ○
- Ⓒ ○
- Ⓑ ●
- Ⓓ ■

20 Four students are standing in line to buy tickets for the craft fair. Marie is standing directly behind John. Amy is standing between John and Fran. Who is first in line?
- Ⓕ Amy
- Ⓖ Fran
- Ⓗ John
- Ⓙ Marie

HINT: Try each answer choice to find the one that is correct.

Directions

For questions 21–25, write or draw your answer to each problem.

21   Look at the number line. Write the number that should go under each mark on the line.

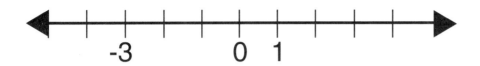

22   Ben was putting tiles on the kitchen floor. He used 64 tiles to finish $\frac{1}{5}$ of the floor. Draw a picture showing $\frac{1}{5}$ of the floor done. Then find the number of tiles Ben will need to finish the rest of the floor. (Show your work.)

HINT: Check your answer to be sure it makes sense.

23   Rita created the number sequence below. Write the rule she used to create her sequence.

1, 3, 7, 15, 31, 63. . .

Scholastic Professional Books

24 This map from a video game does <u>not</u> show the location of the Wizard's Castle. Eduardo knows that the castle is 3 miles south of Dragon Rock and $2\frac{1}{2}$ miles east of Dark Cave. Draw a dot on the map showing where the castle is located and label it Wizard's Castle. (Use an inch ruler to help solve this problem.)

How far is the castle from the Hut on Black Lagoon? _____

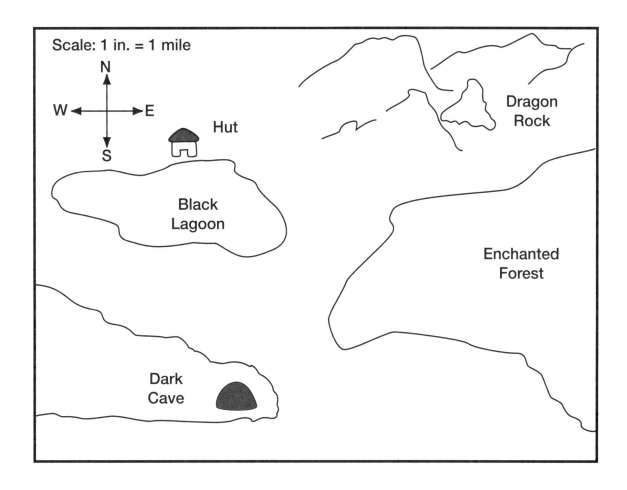

25 Using the map above, write a story problem that uses addition. The answer to the problem should be "8 miles." Then show how to solve the problem.

HINT: Check your work.

_____

_____

_____

Scholastic Professional Books

Mathematics: Practice Test

Part 2

Directions
Choose the best answer to each question. If your answer is not given, mark "None of these."

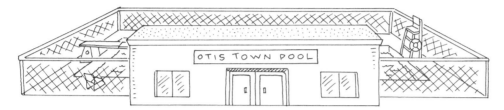

The table below shows the number of people at the Otis Town Pool at each hour on a Friday in July. Use the table to answer questions 26–28.

Time	Number of People
10:00 A.M.	7
11:00 A.M.	13
12:00 NOON	27
1:00 P.M.	55
2:00 P.M.	68
3:00 P.M.	59
4:00 P.M.	32
5:00 P.M.	21

HINT: Look back at the table to find the information you need.

26 At which time was the pool most crowded?
- (F) 10:00 A.M.
- (G) 12:00 NOON
- (H) 2:00 P.M.
- (J) 4:00 P.M.

27 <u>About</u> how many people were probably at the pool at 11:30 A.M.?
- (A) 5
- (B) 20
- (C) 45
- (D) 60

28 Which of these graphs best shows how the number of people at the pool changed during the day?

(F)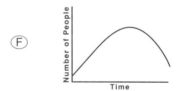

(G)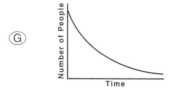

(H)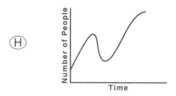

(J)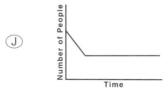

Scholastic Professional Books

29 The rectangular Otis Town Pool is 60 feet long and 25 feet wide. What is the perimeter of the pool?

Ⓐ 50 ft

Ⓑ 85 ft

Ⓒ 110 ft

Ⓓ 175 ft

Ⓔ None of these

HINT: Eliminate any answers that you know are wrong. Then make your best guess.

30 What is the area of the pool?

Ⓕ 85 sq ft

Ⓖ 170 sq ft

Ⓗ 340 sq ft

Ⓙ 1500 sq ft

Ⓚ None of these

Directions

The spring art show for works done by fifth graders will be at the local library. Do questions 31–35 about the art show.

31 Curtis designed this banner for the art show.

Which of these could be the same banner?

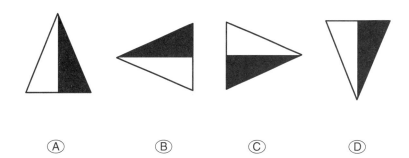

Ⓐ   Ⓑ   Ⓒ   Ⓓ

32 Sophie made some folded paper figures for the art show. In which figure is the dotted line a line of symmetry?

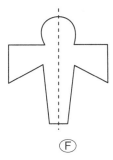   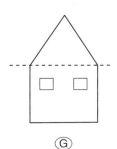   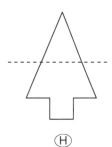   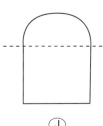

Ⓕ   Ⓖ   Ⓗ   Ⓙ

33 Keith made a metal sculpture in the shape of a triangular prism. How many faces does the prism have?

- Ⓐ 3
- Ⓑ 5
- Ⓒ 6
- Ⓓ 8

ḤINT: Read each problem carefully to make sure you know what it is asking for.

34 Cleo's art project was a cylinder made of recycled plastic. Which of these could be Cleo's project?

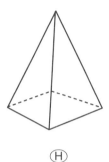
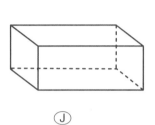

Ⓕ   Ⓖ   Ⓗ   Ⓙ

35 LaToya made four tiles for the art show. Which tile has exactly two parallel sides?

Ⓐ   Ⓑ   Ⓒ   Ⓓ

36 Which of these is congruent to Figure 1?

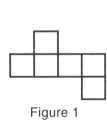

Figure 1

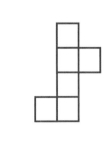
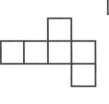
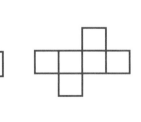

Ⓕ   Ⓖ   Ⓗ   Ⓙ

37 Which number equals the expression shown in the box?

$$(5 \times 10{,}000) + (8 \times 100) + (3 \times 10) + 7$$

Ⓐ 58,307
Ⓑ 50,837
Ⓒ 58,317
Ⓓ 5837

38 Bridget wanted to paint her bedroom a light purple color. In a large bucket she mixed 2 quarts of blue paint, 2 quarts of red paint, and 1 quart of white paint. How many gallons of light purple paint did Bridget make?

Ⓕ 1 gal
Ⓖ $1\frac{1}{4}$ gal
Ⓗ $1\frac{1}{2}$ gal
Ⓙ 2 gal

39 The drive from Springdale to Upton takes 2 hours and 40 minutes. If Mr. Walker arrived in Upton at 9:55 A.M., what time did he leave Springdale?

Ⓐ 8:05 A.M.
Ⓑ 7:40 A.M.
Ⓒ 7:25 A.M.
Ⓓ 7:15 A.M.

HINT: Write a number sentence to help you solve each problem.

40 Ms. Eichler had a five dollar bill, a one dollar bill, 2 quarters, and 7 dimes. Then she paid $3.50 to buy a magazine. How much money did Ms. Eichler have left?

Ⓕ $3.70
Ⓖ $3.50
Ⓗ $2.70
Ⓙ $2.50

41 The small flower pot is 8 inches tall. About how tall is the large flower pot?

Ⓐ 1 ft
Ⓑ $1\frac{1}{2}$ ft
Ⓒ 2 ft
Ⓓ $2\frac{1}{2}$ ft

42 Carl is squeezing oranges for orange juice. He can squeeze 4 to 6 ounces of juice from a single orange. How much juice can he squeeze from 15 oranges?

    Ⓕ between 20 and 30 ounces

    Ⓖ between 40 and 60 ounces

    Ⓗ between 60 and 90 ounces

    Ⓙ between 100 and 150 ounces

HINT: Eliminate any answers that you know are wrong. Then make your best guess.

43 The table shows the height of four students. What is their average height?

    Ⓐ 4' 11"

    Ⓑ 4' 10"

    Ⓒ 4' 9"

    Ⓓ 4' 7"

Student	Height
Amy	4'8"
Carl	4'10"
Mack	4'6"
Brianne	5'0"

44 Frank, Jane, Micah, and Ruth each measured the length of their little fingers. Ruth's little finger was 4.4 cm long. Which mark on the ruler shows the length of Ruth's finger?

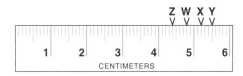

    Ⓕ W

    Ⓖ X

    Ⓗ Y

    Ⓙ Z

45 Kyle and his friends are building a human pyramid. There are 10 people all together. How many rows of people will be in the pyramid?

    Ⓐ 3

    Ⓑ 4

    Ⓒ 5

    Ⓓ 6

HINT: Draw your own picture if it will help you solve the problem.

Directions

For questions 46–50, write or draw your answer to each problem.

46   Use a centimeter ruler to find the length of each side of this mailing label. Write your answers.

HINT: Check your work.

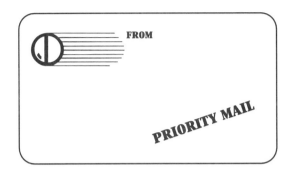

At a school fair, students made the board shown below. Each person who plays the Beanbag Toss game throws one beanbag onto the board. Use this information to answer questions 47 and 48.

Beanbag Toss

HINT: Check your answer to be sure it makes sense.

1	2	3	4	5	6	7	8	9	10
11	12	13	14	15	16	17	18	19	20
21	22	23	24	25	26	27	28	29	30
31	32	33	34	35	36	37	38	39	40
41	42	43	44	45	46	47	48	49	50

47   If Kayla throws one beanbag onto the board, what is the probability that it will land on an even number? (Show your work.)

48   What is the probability that the beanbag will land on a number divisible by 5? (Show your work.)

Scholastic Professional Books

Music Land sold 220 CDs in one week. The pictograph below shows how many CDs were sold each day. Use this information to answer questions 49 and 50.

HINT: Read each problem carefully to make sure you know what it is asking for.

CDs Sold at Music Land	
Day	Number of CDs Sold
Monday	◉ ◉ ◉ ◖
Tuesday	◉ ◉ ◉ ◉
Wednesday	◉ ◉ ◉
Thursday	◉ ◉ ◉ ◉ ◖
Friday	◉ ◉
Saturday	◉ ◉ ◉ ◉ ◉

49 One ◉ represents how many CDs? (Show your work.)

50 On the grid below, make a bar graph showing the number of CDs sold each day. Include labels and a title.

ANSWER SHEET

Student Name _____ Grade _____

Teacher Name _____ Date _____

Reading/Language Arts Samples

A Ⓐ Ⓑ Ⓒ Ⓓ   E Ⓐ Ⓑ Ⓒ Ⓓ
B Ⓕ Ⓖ Ⓗ Ⓙ   F Ⓕ Ⓖ Ⓗ Ⓙ
C Ⓐ Ⓑ Ⓒ Ⓓ   G Ⓐ Ⓑ Ⓒ Ⓓ
D Ⓕ Ⓖ Ⓗ Ⓙ   H Ⓕ Ⓖ Ⓗ Ⓙ

Mathematics Samples

A Ⓐ Ⓑ Ⓒ Ⓓ Ⓔ
B Ⓕ Ⓖ Ⓗ Ⓙ Ⓚ
C Ⓐ Ⓑ Ⓒ Ⓓ Ⓔ
D Ⓕ Ⓖ Ⓗ Ⓙ Ⓚ

Practice Test, Part 1

1 Ⓐ Ⓑ Ⓒ Ⓓ
2 Ⓕ Ⓖ Ⓗ Ⓙ
3 Ⓐ Ⓑ Ⓒ Ⓓ
4 Ⓕ Ⓖ Ⓗ Ⓙ
5 Ⓐ Ⓑ Ⓒ Ⓓ
6 Ⓕ Ⓖ Ⓗ Ⓙ
7 Ⓐ Ⓑ Ⓒ Ⓓ
8 Ⓕ Ⓖ Ⓗ Ⓙ
9 Ⓐ Ⓑ Ⓒ Ⓓ
10 Ⓕ Ⓖ Ⓗ Ⓙ
11 Ⓐ Ⓑ Ⓒ Ⓓ
12 Ⓕ Ⓖ Ⓗ Ⓙ
13 Ⓐ Ⓑ Ⓒ Ⓓ
14 Ⓕ Ⓖ Ⓗ Ⓙ
15 Ⓐ Ⓑ Ⓒ Ⓓ
16 Ⓕ Ⓖ Ⓗ Ⓙ
17 Ⓐ Ⓑ Ⓒ Ⓓ
18 Ⓕ Ⓖ Ⓗ Ⓙ
19 Ⓐ Ⓑ Ⓒ Ⓓ
20 Ⓕ Ⓖ Ⓗ Ⓙ

Practice Test, Part 2

26 Ⓕ Ⓖ Ⓗ Ⓙ
27 Ⓐ Ⓑ Ⓒ Ⓓ
28 Ⓕ Ⓖ Ⓗ Ⓙ
29 Ⓐ Ⓑ Ⓒ Ⓓ
30 Ⓕ Ⓖ Ⓗ Ⓙ
31 Ⓐ Ⓑ Ⓒ Ⓓ
32 Ⓕ Ⓖ Ⓗ Ⓙ
33 Ⓐ Ⓑ Ⓒ Ⓓ
34 Ⓕ Ⓖ Ⓗ Ⓙ
35 Ⓐ Ⓑ Ⓒ Ⓓ
36 Ⓕ Ⓖ Ⓗ Ⓙ
37 Ⓐ Ⓑ Ⓒ Ⓓ
38 Ⓕ Ⓖ Ⓗ Ⓙ
39 Ⓐ Ⓑ Ⓒ Ⓓ
40 Ⓕ Ⓖ Ⓗ Ⓙ
41 Ⓐ Ⓑ Ⓒ Ⓓ
42 Ⓕ Ⓖ Ⓗ Ⓙ
43 Ⓐ Ⓑ Ⓒ Ⓓ
44 Ⓕ Ⓖ Ⓗ Ⓙ
45 Ⓐ Ⓑ Ⓒ Ⓓ

Practice Test, Part 1

1 Ⓐ Ⓑ Ⓒ Ⓓ Ⓔ
2 Ⓕ Ⓖ Ⓗ Ⓙ Ⓚ
3 Ⓐ Ⓑ Ⓒ Ⓓ Ⓔ
4 Ⓕ Ⓖ Ⓗ Ⓙ Ⓚ
5 Ⓐ Ⓑ Ⓒ Ⓓ Ⓔ
6 Ⓕ Ⓖ Ⓗ Ⓙ Ⓚ
7 Ⓐ Ⓑ Ⓒ Ⓓ Ⓔ
8 Ⓕ Ⓖ Ⓗ Ⓙ Ⓚ
9 Ⓐ Ⓑ Ⓒ Ⓓ Ⓔ
10 Ⓕ Ⓖ Ⓗ Ⓙ Ⓚ
11 Ⓐ Ⓑ Ⓒ Ⓓ Ⓔ
12 Ⓕ Ⓖ Ⓗ Ⓙ Ⓚ
13 Ⓐ Ⓑ Ⓒ Ⓓ Ⓔ
14 Ⓕ Ⓖ Ⓗ Ⓙ Ⓚ
15 Ⓐ Ⓑ Ⓒ Ⓓ Ⓔ
16 Ⓕ Ⓖ Ⓗ Ⓙ Ⓚ
17 Ⓐ Ⓑ Ⓒ Ⓓ Ⓔ
18 Ⓕ Ⓖ Ⓗ Ⓙ Ⓚ
19 Ⓐ Ⓑ Ⓒ Ⓓ Ⓔ
20 Ⓕ Ⓖ Ⓗ Ⓙ Ⓚ

Practice Test, Part 2

26 Ⓕ Ⓖ Ⓗ Ⓙ Ⓚ
27 Ⓐ Ⓑ Ⓒ Ⓓ Ⓔ
28 Ⓕ Ⓖ Ⓗ Ⓙ Ⓚ
29 Ⓐ Ⓑ Ⓒ Ⓓ Ⓔ
30 Ⓕ Ⓖ Ⓗ Ⓙ Ⓚ
31 Ⓐ Ⓑ Ⓒ Ⓓ Ⓔ
32 Ⓕ Ⓖ Ⓗ Ⓙ Ⓚ
33 Ⓐ Ⓑ Ⓒ Ⓓ Ⓔ
34 Ⓕ Ⓖ Ⓗ Ⓙ Ⓚ
35 Ⓐ Ⓑ Ⓒ Ⓓ Ⓔ
36 Ⓕ Ⓖ Ⓗ Ⓙ Ⓚ
37 Ⓐ Ⓑ Ⓒ Ⓓ Ⓔ
38 Ⓕ Ⓖ Ⓗ Ⓙ Ⓚ
39 Ⓐ Ⓑ Ⓒ Ⓓ Ⓔ
40 Ⓕ Ⓖ Ⓗ Ⓙ Ⓚ
41 Ⓐ Ⓑ Ⓒ Ⓓ Ⓔ
42 Ⓕ Ⓖ Ⓗ Ⓙ Ⓚ
43 Ⓐ Ⓑ Ⓒ Ⓓ Ⓔ
44 Ⓕ Ⓖ Ⓗ Ⓙ Ⓚ
45 Ⓐ Ⓑ Ⓒ Ⓓ Ⓔ

Scholastic Professional Books

Answer Keys

Reading/Language Arts
Practice Test, Part 1

1.	D	11.	C
2.	G	12.	G
3.	A	13.	A
4.	H	14.	J
5.	D	15.	B
6.	G	16.	F
7.	C	17.	D
8.	H	18.	J
9.	D	19.	A
10.	F	20.	G

21. Answers may vary. Example: Deer were eating the vegetables in their garden.

22. Answers may vary. Example: At first they thought Grandma's idea was silly. A few days later, they were pleased to realize that it worked.

23. Answers will vary. Example: There were too many shoemakers in the city, so no one bought Jacob's shoes. When two mice chewed holes in all his shoes, he sold them as sandals.

24. Answers will vary. Example: Grandpa and Josh tried a new idea to keep deer out of their garden, and it worked. Jacob could not sell his shoes, but after they were ruined he sold them as sandals instead.

25.

> Dear ~~mom and dad~~. **Mom and Dad,**
>
> The train ride was ~~fun~~ **fun,** but it was very long. When I arrived in Boston on ~~saturday~~ **Saturday**, Uncle Harry met me at the station. "~~Its~~ **It's** wonderful to see ~~you~~ **you,"** he ~~said."~~ **said,"** I was glad to see him, too.
>
> ~~love always~~ **Love always,**
> Miranda

Reading/Language Arts
Practice Test, Part 2

26.	G	36.	F
27.	C	37.	B
28.	J	38.	J
29.	B	39.	A
30.	F	40.	G
31.	D	41.	C
32.	J	42.	J
33.	A	43.	D
34.	H	44.	G
35.	B	45.	A

46. Answers may vary. Example: He thought it was important for her to win but also to have fun.

47. Answers will vary. Example: Venus Williams is talented, and she has confidence in herself.

48. Answers may vary. Example: Mr. Williamson said that he would clear a lot behind the store and donate cement to build a skating area.

49. Tryouts will be held on Saturday, September 10, at 10:00 A.M. at the Norwich Elementary School.

50. Parents who want to help coach the team should attend the first tryout. Possibly, students might also mention that parents need to sign permission forms.

Scholastic Professional Books

**Mathematics
Practice Test, Part 1**

1. D	11. B
2. H	12. F
3. C	13. B
4. F	14. H
5. B	15. C
6. G	16. F
7. E	17. E
8. J	18. J
9. D	19. B
10. H	20. G

21.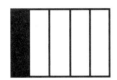

22. Example:

Ben used 64 tiles for $\frac{1}{5}$ of the floor, so he will use a total of 320 tiles (5×64) on the entire floor. He needs 256 tiles ($320 - 64$) to finish the rest of the floor.

23. Starting with 1, the rule is "double the number and add 1." The rule may be written as an algebraic expression, such as $2n + 1$.

24. Wizard's Castle should be located 3 in. below Dragon Rock and $2\frac{1}{2}$ in. right of Dark Cave. It is 4 miles from the Hut.

25. <u>Example problem</u> : Queen Zelda rode from Dragon Rock to the Hut on Black Lagoon. Then she rode to the Dark Cave, picked up a magic stone, and rode back to the Hut. How far did she ride in all?
<u>Solution</u> : 3 in + $2\frac{1}{2}$ in + $2\frac{1}{2}$ in = 8 in.
The scale is 1 in = 1 mile, so she rode 8 miles.

**Mathematics
Practice Test, Part 2**

26. H	36. F
27. B	37. B
28. F	38. G
29. E	39. D
30. J	40. F
31. D	41. C
32. F	42. H
33. B	43. C
34. G	44. J
35. A	45. B

46. The label is 7 cm × 4 cm.

47. There are 50 numbers on the board, and 25 of them are even. The probability of landing on an even number is $\frac{25}{50}$, or $\frac{1}{2}$, or 50%.

48. Of the 50 numbers, 10 are divisible by 5. The probability of landing on a number divisible by 5 is $\frac{10}{50}$, or $\frac{1}{5}$, or 20%.

49. One ⊙ = 10 CDs. Explanations may vary. Example: A total of 220 CDs were sold in one week. The total number of icons is 22, so I divided $\frac{220}{22}$ = 10.

50. Answers may vary. Example:

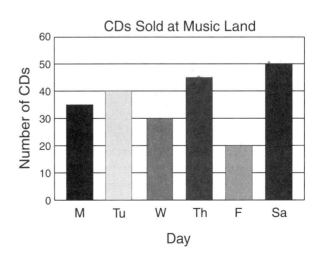

Scoring Chart

Student Name _____ **Grade** _____

Teacher Name _____ **Date** _____

Directions: For each part of the test, count the number of questions answered correctly. Write the "Number Correct" in the box. To find the Percentage Score, divide the "Number Correct" by the "Total" number of questions. For example, 40 correct out of 50 questions = 40 ÷ 50, which is 0.8, or 80%.

	Number Correct/Total	Percentage Score
Reading/Language Arts **Practice Test**		
Part 1: Questions 1–25	/25	
Part 2: Questions 26–50	/25	
Total Reading/Language Arts	/50	
Mathematics **Practice Test**		
Part 1: Questions 1–25	/25	
Part 2: Questions 26–50	/25	
Total Mathematics	/50	